PICKLE

MISS SCORCHER'S DESERT LESSONS

Valerie Wilding

illustrated by
Kelly Waldek

For my dear friend S   ob
with love.

Scholastic Children's Books,
Commonwealth House, 1-19 New Oxford Street,
London WC1A

A division of Scholastic Ltd
London ~ New York ~ Toronto ~ Sydney ~ Auckland
Mexico City ~ New Delhi ~ Hong Kong

Published in the UK by Scholastic Ltd, 2002

Text copyright © Valerie Wilding, 2002
Illustrations copyright © Kelly Waldek, 2002

ISBN 0 439 99953 7

Typeset by M Rules
Printed by Cox & Wyman Ltd, Reading, Berks

2 4 6 8 10 9 7 5 3 1

Contents

WELCOME To PICKLE HILL PRIMARY

Hi! I'm Tess Taylor, I was going to draw a picture of Pickle Hill, but – why bother? On the outside, it looks just like any other school. Yours, maybe!

But when you open the doors and come inside, you'll see that there's absolutely, completely and definitely nothing ordinary about Pickle Hill Primary.

We have the best teachers ever but – are they weird or what! They're all nuts about their favourite topics, and when a Pickle Hill Primary teacher gives a lesson, funny things happen! For instance, you have cupboards, right? So do we, but when we open them, we never know what's likely to jump out. And as for our computer. . . !

Why not join me and my class for double geography with Miss Scorcher, then you'll really see what I mean!

☆Tess☆

PICKLE HILL PRIMARY

Teacher's name: Miss Sandy Scorcher

Age: Over 21 (she says)

Appearance: I think she's really beautiful

Subject: Geography

Favourite topic:
Deserts — she says they're hot stuff!

Quirks:
Always on the go — a fast mover!

Information supplied by:

Tess Taylor, Class 5F

Rain dance

Bang! Bang! Bang!

Someone was kicking the classroom door. Lizzie tiptoed across and put her ear to it. She nearly fell over when there was another bang and a muffled voice called, "Let me in!"

Lizzie flung the door open. "It's Miss Scorcher!"

Miss Scorcher dumped her stuff on the floor, untied the bags from her belt and tossed them into a corner. Thud! Thud!

"Phew! Our new geography topic," she said, "is all about my favourite places – any guesses?"

"You need a clue," said Miss Scorcher. "These places are very, very big, and very, very dry, and –"

Everybody screeched at once. "Deserts!"

"That's right, deserts it is!" beamed Miss Scorcher.

"It'll be a short lesson, then," said Gordon. "We already know all there is to know."

"Oh yes?" said Miss Scorcher. "What do you know, Gordon?"

"I know that nothing lives there and nothing grows there. There's only sand and we all know what sand is."

"That's a start," said Miss Scorcher. "But by the time we've finished, you'll know so much about the desert you'd be able to write a book about it!"

"Imagine being in the desert," Meena said dreamily. "Bikini, sun hat, iced drink, magazine…"

"What exactly are deserts?" I asked.

"Just the question I was hoping for!" said Miss Scorcher.

Flip! That was a first!

"Deserts," she said, "are places where there's very little moisture. Hang on a sec!" She held out her hand. "It's going to rain."

Will Baker looked up. A large drop of water plopped on his nose. "It *is* raining!" he said.

And it was!

"Isn't this lesson supposed to be about deserts?" I yelled, and tried to hop on to a chair. I had my brand-new trainers on. At least, I thought I did. When I looked down, I was wearing wellies. So was everyone else.

We went a bit daft! We'd never had rain in our classroom before!

As suddenly as it started, it stopped.

"This," said Miss Scorcher, "is the maximum amount of rain that falls in the desert – in one year."

"Blimey!" said Lizzie. "It's not much."

"I'll measure it," said Gordon. He splashed over to the tray unit for a ruler. He sploshed back – and I mean *sploshed* because, being Gordon, he can't do anything simple without knocking something over. He tried to jump over the bin, slipped, and the something he knocked over was me! Splosh!

"Gordon, you clumsy dope!" I yelled. "I'm drowned!"

Hiroko sniggered. "Tess's hair's calmed down for once!"

25cm isn't a lot.

Will worries about everything.

"On average, we get about five times that amount," said Miss Scorcher.

Will frowned. "Over a whole year, 25 centimetres is hardly a splash – not much for a plant."

"I told you," said Gordon. "Nothing can grow in a desert."

"Twenty-five centimetres isn't much," said Miss Scorcher, "and it certainly is tough for most living things. Incredibly, though, many things do survive, as we'll see. Tess, fetch the globe, please."

"Shouldn't we get dry first?" I asked.

Miss Scorcher grinned. "You are dry."

I had my trainers on again, and the water

was dwindling to a puddle. The puddle shrank and disappeared.

"I bet some deserts don't even get that much rain, do they, Miss Scorcher?" asked Ben Lee.

"That's right," she said. "The Atacama Desert, in South America, went for 400 years without any rain – so it's believed."

"Long time to go without a drink!" said Nita, who couldn't go more than an hour without some form of nourishment.

"If you got lost in the Atacama you'd die of thirst," Lizzie hissed, "and you'd get picked at by vultures and end up a pile of dry white bones." She crashed to the floor, tongue hanging out, gasping.

We all fell about. Even Miss Scorcher's lips twitched. "Does anyone know how much of our world is desert?" she asked.

No one answered.

"Then make some space. It's time for a spin." Miss Scorcher looked at me. "Tess? The globe?"

"Oops, I forgot." I fetched it.

A spin? What on earth was she on about?

Global warming!

We pushed the desks out of the way and gathered round, while Miss Scorcher spun the globe. It whirled faster and faster until it was almost a blur. It whizzed so fast that it blew Meena's fringe upwards. Then it slowed, and stopped.

"Wow!" I said. "It's changed!"

The sea was still blue, and the land still green, but there were no cities marked, no rivers, no names at all – just some bright yellow patches here and there.

"Those blobs must be deserts," said Gordon.

"What a lot of blobs," said Will.

We worked out roughly how much of the land was desert. Most of us reckoned over a quarter, maybe as much as a third.

"And there's desert all over – even in Australia," said Gordon. "Look." He knelt down, then toppled over and grabbed the globe to steady himself.

Ow! It's hot!

"Yes," said Miss Scorcher. "You've put your hand on the Sahara Desert, in Africa." She took a thermometer out of her bag.

The Sahara holds the record for the hottest temperature ever recorded – nearly 58°c in the shade.

"That's twice as hot as a roasting summer's day," said Freddie.

"And that was the air temperature," said Miss Scorcher. "The temperature on the ground, where there's very little air movement, can be as high as 82°C."

"I bet that's hot enough to fry an egg," said Meena.

"How would you know?" said Hiroko. "You never even make toast!"

Hiroko and Meena are next-door neighbours, and they're always having a go at each other.

"Meena's right," said Miss Scorcher. "82°C is certainly hot enough to cook an egg!"

"Are all deserts that hot?" I asked.

"Feel the globe, Tess."

I did, very carefully! I didn't want a shock like Gordon had. The deserts round the middle of the globe, near the Equator, were hot, but the Antarctic, down at the South Pole, felt cold.

"How can the Antarctic be a desert?" I asked. "It's all ice, and ice is water."

"Yeah, but it's frozen water," said Gordon. "No plants or trees can grow in ice."

"That's right," said Miss Scorcher, "and the rainfall – or snowfall, in this case – is so low that the Antarctic qualifies as a desert."

An argument broke out as to whether it was better to be in a hot or a cold desert.

"Ice deserts aren't the only cold deserts," said Miss Scorcher. "Some, such as the Kalahari in Africa, are hot in summer but pretty chilly in winter."

"Like my bedroom!" said Gordon.

Sonoran:
hot summer,
chilly winter.

Sahara:
hot summer,
cold winter,
biggest desert
in the world.

Atacama:
warm, but 10
years without
rain is normal.

Namib:
hot inland,
cooler near
the coast,
some sand
dunes are as
long as 300
football
pitches.

Antarctica:
perishing cold all year
round, horribly windy,
lowest temperature ever
recorded: −89.2°c

"You can see that even the hottest deserts can be bitterly cold at night," Miss Scorcher said. "And your homework is to find out why."

clouds   clouds   clouds

Warm air rising   Warm air rising

My house in summer. The clouds stop warm air escaping. It's warm, but dark.

hot air rising   hot air rising

The desert. No clouds, so heat can escape. After the sun goes down, it soon gets cold. Brrr! by Tess.

Miss Scorcher beetled to the door. "See you!" she called, and whooshed out, banging the door behind her.

She'd forgotten all her stuff, so I ran after her. Luckily, I stopped in time to avoid a squashed nose, because the door flew open and Miss Scorcher stuck her head back in. "Don't worry, Tess, it can stay till next lesson," she said – as if she'd read my mind. "By the way, everybody – expect a very special visitor."

"Who could that be?" I wondered.

Lizzie smirked. "Bet it's her lover boy!"

Arizona Joe

Miss Scorcher whizzed across the room with the computer trolley, and skidded to a stop. "Let's look at a real desert!"

Our chairs made a perfect semicircle round the computer – by themselves! We sat down.

Miss Scorcher shoved in a CD and up came three icons. She moved the cursor past the corner of the screen. When it turned into a double-headed arrow, she left-clicked and dragged. The whole thing grew bigger. Not just the screen – the monitor too!

A snake slithered across the screen. Lizzie went, "All *right*!" but two people yelped. Will, beside me, shivered.

A deep voice behind us said, "Don't you mind that pesky critter. He ain't gonna hurt you – not unless you make him mad."

We spun round. Sitting in the teacher's chair, with his filthy boots on her desk was … well, see for yourself.

"Why would I want a gun?" said the man. "I'm here to tell you about my home. Right, Miss Sandy?"

"Right, Arizona Joe."

"Woo hoo!" Lizzie went in my ear. "Miss Sandy, eh? Maybe he *is* her boyfriend!"

I snorted with laughter at the thought.

He jerked his thumb towards the screen.

The Sonoran Desert. 310,000 square kilometres – that's 120,000 square miles. Nearly as big as the UK and Ireland put together. The biggest and best desert in the whole of the United States, in my opinion – even though part of it's in Mexico. Click on whatever takes your fancy.

Lizzie dived for "Monster".

"Ho ho," said Arizona Joe. "That there's a Gila monster."

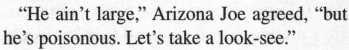

"Huh!" said Lizzie. "Not what I'd call a monster."

"He ain't large," Arizona Joe agreed, "but he's poisonous. Let's take a look-see."

Joe strolled over to the screen, and picked up the Gila monster.

We were too surprised to be scared!

"Plump little fella, ain't he?" said Arizona Joe proudly. "This lizard here grows to about

60 centimetres. He's black, but those markings can be pink or orange. He stores fat in that chunky tail, and he can go more'n a year without eating."

Nita looked ill at the thought.

"Is he vicious?" asked Lizzie.

"He would be, if you riled him, but you don't wanna do that – his bite's poisonous. He's not too fast, though, so I reckon you'd get away from him before he did too much damage."

"Meena wouldn't," said Hiroko. "She never moves fast."

"Nah!" said Lizzie. "I reckon that Gila monster would sink its nasty vicious little teeth into Meena's –"

"Lizzie!" said Miss Scorcher. "Not in front of visitors." She smiled sweetly at Joe. "Some more reptiles?"

"Whatever you say, Miss Sandy."

The boys nudged each other. "He'd do anything for her when she looks at him like that!" giggled Arnie Peasmarsh.

Joe put the Gila monster back *into* the screen. "Look what's coming."

A snake appeared, spotted the Gila and waved its tail with a rattling sound.

"Yep, that's the rattlesnake," grunted Arizona Joe. "His rattle warns you to stay away. He doesn't want to eat you – he'd rather have a tasty rat. Swallow it whole, no trouble at all. Hey! Look out!"

"No, no, not you," laughed Arizona Joe. "I'm talking to the rattler. Yo! King snake coming! Git goin'!"

"Don't go, rattler!" yelled Lizzie. "Bite him!"

Joe laughed. "He wouldn't dare."

"Not everyone likes snakes, Joe," said Miss Scorcher, eyeing a few pale faces, "but I'm sure you've got lots more to show us!"

"Just click on 'Critters' if you please, Miss S, ma'am," said Arizona Joe.

"Critters?" said Will.

"It's Joe's word for 'creatures'." Miss Scorcher stretched for the mouse.

"I'll do it," said Gordon. He dived for the computer, tripped and thumped the keyboard with his elbow.

A blue error message appeared.

"Oh oh," said Miss Scorcher.

A line of animals
moved across the
screen. "Doggone it!"
said Arizona Joe.
"Mind yer feet, y'all!"

Hopping, running and crawling, the animals
reached the screen's edge. Instead of
vanishing, they dropped straight on to the
nearest object – Freddie.

Freddie's pretty fit. We're used to him
leaping over chairs and stuff – but we've
never seen him clear a desk in one bound
before.

Mind you, within seconds we'd all shifted –
the floor was alive with paws and claws! Half
the class was on chairs and the other half, led
by Lizzie, was in there amid the fur and
scales.

"Hey, go easy on them there critters," said Arizona Joe. "You gotta treat them with respect, otherwise you're gonna make 'em *really* wild."

I eyed a scorpion that was investigating Miss Scorcher's boots. I wouldn't like to make *him* wild. I kept well clear.

Arizona Joe saw my face. "Don't worry – they ain't gonna hurt you while I'm here. Go on, make friends, see what you can learn."

THE HORNED LIZARD

The horned lizard blends into its background, so it's hard to spot.

Threaten it, and it might squirt blood at you – from its eyes. Cool!
by Lizzie West

I liked the fox. It was called a kit fox, and it was hard to catch because it was so fast.

"He needs speed to catch a tasty rat or rabbit," said Joe.

"His ears are huge," I said. "Do they help him hear his prey?"

"Yup," said Joe, "and they help keep him cool. His blood flows through the ears, and they give off heat."

"Like water in a radiator," I said – cleverly, I thought.

Joe shrugged. "If you say so, little lady."

Well, I don't suppose he'd ever seen a radiator.

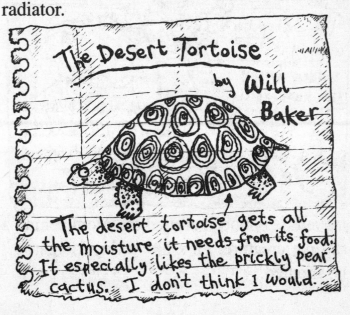

The Desert Tortoise
by Will Baker

The desert tortoise gets all the moisture it needs from its food. It especially likes the prickly pear cactus. I don't think I would.

Penny White cooed over a rabbit with enormous ears. "It's a jack rabbit," she told me. "These ears listen for enemies when he's feeding at night."

"And they act like radiators," I said, "to keep him cool."

"Don't be daft," she said. "Radiators keep you warm."

Honestly, she just didn't get it.

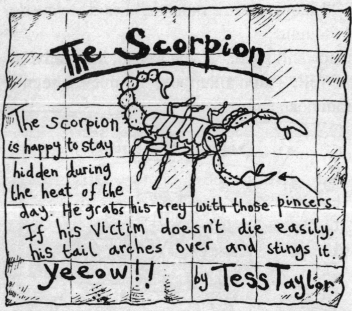

The Scorpion

The scorpion is happy to stay hidden during the heat of the day. He grabs his prey with those pincers. If his victim doesn't die easily, his tail arches over and stings it. yeeow!! by Tess Taylor.

Freddie bounced around the room behind a rat-like creature. "It's like a tiny kangaroo," he shouted.

"That kangaroo rat's well-adapted to the desert," said Joe. "He doesn't need much water, and those strong legs help him dig a cool, safe burrow."

I wondered if they had kangaroo rats in Australia, where there are proper kangaroos, but Joe said no. "Every desert has its own plants and animals," he explained.

"Why?" asked Freddie.

"Because each desert has different conditions, so the plants and animals have adapted to cope with their own environments. Oh oh!" he said. "Here comes another American native!"

We spun round as something whizzed right across the computer screen.

"What on earth was *that*?" Freddie asked.

Arizona Joe laughed. "You got a 'freeze' type doo-dad on that thing, ma'am?"

As the thing streaked back the other way, Miss Scorcher clicked.

"A roadrunner!" I said.

"Right," said Joe. "That bird's an awkward flier, and soon gets tired. On foot, though, he's *fast*. Twenty-five kilometres an hour's nothing to him when he's hunting lunch. Roadrunners used to like chasing after horses or stagecoaches, gobbling up the insects they disturbed."

Miss Scorcher jumped up. "We must be fast, too," she said. "Gather your critters, please, Joe."

He jerked his thumb at the monitor. "Critters? Git back!"

The animals leapt into the screen.

Arnie Peasmarsh stared. "See that? They gitted!"

Zooop!

"Let's see something cute." Joe clicked on "Forest".

A tall cactus appeared, then another, and another. The screen quickly filled with cacti. When it was full to bursting, one sprouted in our classroom!

First a bulge in the floor tiles, a push, and then it burst through…

Zooop!

Oww!

Watch that branch!

Look at the size of that!

"The saguaro cactus can grow 15 metres high," said Joe, "but that takes a long, long time."

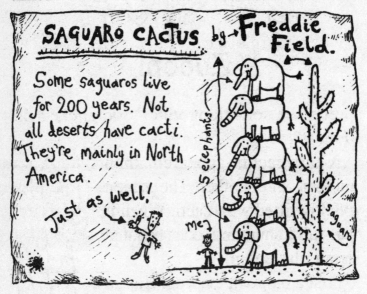

"Why does the icon say 'Forest'?" I asked.

"Well, let me tell you," said Arizona Joe, "there truly are whole forests of saguaros where I come from. Other cacti, too."

"But it's still desert," I asked, "even though there are lots of plants?"

"Sure is. The Sonoran Desert doesn't get much rain, but lookee here." Joe pointed to the cactus. "This stem's tough and mighty thick," he said. "It holds a store of water for

the plant, and when it gets the chance to fill up, those ridges swell out and make even more room."

"How can one plant get so much water when there's hardly any rain?" Ben Lee asked.

Joe winked. "Saguaros are crafty! They let their roots travel over a wide area, just below the surface of the ground. See?"

And we did. See, I mean! As we looked down where he was pointing, the floor disappeared! Well, it didn't disappear exactly, or we'd have fallen through, but we could see right through it!

Those roots can spread up to 15 metres away, so when it does rain, they suck up every drop they can get.

"It's clever," Meena said, "but not cute. You promised cute."

Arizona Joe pointed towards the top of the cactus. "Look closer."

At first we couldn't see what he was on about, but then…

"Look!" cried Gordon, who's tallest. "High up, in that hole!"

"Hey, another hole!" Hiroko pointed.

Arizona Joe chuckled. "I reckon that qualifies as cute."

Meena edged forward. "Is it a miniature woodpecker?"

"Miniature nothing," said Joe. "That's a fully grown elf owl."

Meena tweeted at it. The owl fluttered down to perch on her head.

"If it doesn't eat all day it must be starving by night-time," said Nita. She frowned. "Isn't it lunch now? I'm hungry."

"You always are!" said Hiroko and Meena.

Miss Scorcher checked her watch. "Nita's right," she said. "It's lunchtime."

"Then I'll be off, ma'am," said Arizona Joe. He winked at her.

We all went, "oooOOOOoooo!"

Then he winked at us. "Bye y'all."

Zooop! The cactus disappeared.

Miss Scorcher told us to collect our lunch boxes. When we turned to say goodbye to Arizona Joe, he wasn't there.

"Come on, I'm famished," said Nita.

GILA WOODPECKER

by Tess Taylor.

The Gila woodpecker digs a hole in the saguaro with its beak.

The high nest keeps it safe from enemies.

Its sharp claws help it to hang on to the cactus and its stiff tail supports it like an extra leg.

Juicy red cactus fruit – food!

Eggs stay cool inside the hole.

So do the babies. Aren't they sweet?

Fog and flowers

"Miss Scorcher, your globe's wrong," said Hiroko. "This blob's on the coast so it can't be a desert, can it? It rains a lot at the seaside – at least, it does when we go."

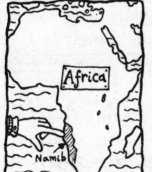

"Aah, poor Hiroko," said Miss Scorcher, patting her on the shoulder. "But that blob's the Namib, and it's a coastal desert. Freddie, can you bring me my sandbags, please?"

The bags looked heavy, even for Freddie. He and Miss Scorcher opened one each and poured the sand on the floor. Freddie's bag soon emptied, but Miss Scorcher's poured on and on until there was a mound as high as her desk.

I suddenly felt very warm. Everything looked misty. I rubbed my eyes. What was going on?

The Namib's not so hot near the coast because air blowing towards it from the sea cools down as it reaches the land, and turns into fog.

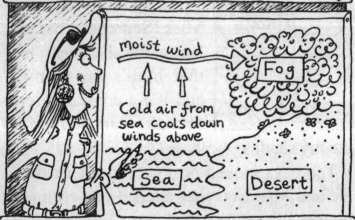

moist wind

Fog

Cold air from sea cools down winds above

Sea

Desert

That moisture is just what's needed by some of the creatures living there — even the odd plant. They manage to get the water they need from the fog.

"How do they get water?" I asked. "You can't drink fog."

"They've adapted to make the most of foggy conditions." Miss Scorcher glanced down. "Watch your feet, Tess."

"Whoa!" I jumped back. A long ribbon of green snaked towards me. Another green ribbon snaked towards Lucy Lee.

The welwitschia's two leaves can be two metres long. They absorb water droplets from the fog. The long, fat root stores moisture, and it does a pretty good job because the welwitschia can live for hundreds of years.

This is a leaf.

That's the root.

Will elbowed me in the ribs and pointed. "Look," he said.

A beetle, nearly as big as my thumb, was steadily making its way through the fog, climbing up the sand hill.

"Don't worry, Will," said Miss Scorcher. "That's a darkling beetle. It lives in the Namib and at the moment it has one thing on its mind. Water!"

The beetle made it to the top of the sand hill, turned to face the fog that rolled over it, and stuck its bottom in the air!

"What's it doing?" I asked.

"As the fog touches its warm shiny back," said Miss Scorcher, "it turns into drops of water which roll down towards the beetle's mouth."

"Like when you boil the kettle near the kitchen window, and your mum moans about the condensation?" said Gordon.

"Exactly."

I thought about this. "I understand about the coastal desert, but what about deserts further inland? If clouds and rain blow from the sea on to the land –"

"Like when I'm on holiday," said Hiroko.

"– then why don't they just keep going and rain on the desert?"

Miss Scorcher beamed. "Another good question, Tess!"

You could have toasted bread on my face!

"Look out of the window," she said.

The playground had vanished, along with the rest of the town!

Far out!

"Those clouds are being blown towards the land," said Miss Scorcher. "Watch what happens."

When the clouds reached the mountains, they burst into a storm of rain. As they moved over the topmost ridges, they were just little white puffs that melted away as they met the heat of the desert.

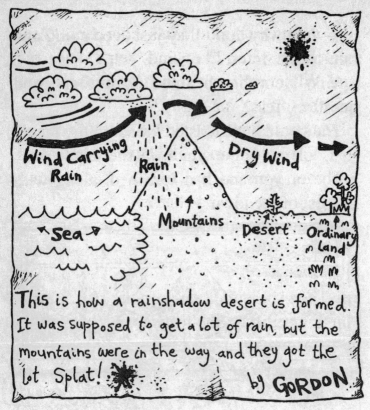

Wind Carrying Rain

Rain

Dry Wind

Sea

Mountains

Desert

Ordinary Land

This is how a rainshadow desert is formed. It was supposed to get a lot of rain, but the mountains were in the way and they got the lot. Splat!

by GORDON

"What about deserts that don't have mountains in the way?" asked Lucy.

"Deserts like the Gobi," said Miss Scorcher, "are such a long way inland that by the time the winds from the sea get there, they've dumped all the rain they were carrying."

"But when deserts do get rain," said Ben, "does it just soak into the ground like this?" He sucked his cheeks in.

46

"Sometimes," said Miss Scorcher. "And sometimes water, like wind, helps shape the land. Whoever's nearest the tray unit, can you pass the top left-hand tray?"

I was nearest. The tray was full of grit and dust. I went to tip it in the bin, but Miss Scorcher was on me like a heat-seeking missile before I had a chance.

"Stop! I want that!" She fished in her bag and took out a pair of goggly-looking glasses. "You'll need these," she said, tossing them to me. Then she pulled out another pair. Carrie Marsh got those. She's always in front when a freebie's being handed out.

Again and again, Miss Scorcher reached into her bag. "Plenty for all," she said.

I put mine on and stared at Meena.

When I looked into the tray I nearly fell over backwards. "Come and see!" I yelled. I felt the others squash in beside me.

There was a hush … then…

And we were – really there, I mean, in the desert. At least, it felt like we were there, and it *looked* like we were there, so it must have been – virtual reality!

And a shower we had! We were hot, so we didn't mind getting wet. The ground seemed to suck up the rain as it fell. When it stopped,

Miss Scorcher said, "Take a look!"

We all turned. Gordon's goggles caught me on the side of the head and by the time I'd straightened my own goggles (and twanged the elastic at the back of his) I was last to see, but there was Miss Scorcher showing us her watch. You could actually see the hands moving. Round and round, then they speeded up, faster and faster, until my eyes went fuzzy.

"What's happening?" cried Will.

"Time's passing," said Miss Scorcher. "We're heading into the future."

Will gasped. "The future?"

"Just a few weeks from now," said Miss Scorcher. "Er, I mean from then ... from when we started, if you see what I mean." The watch hands slowed. "Nearly ... nearly ... NOW!" she yelled.

The hands stopped.

You could have knocked me down with a bunch of daffodils! The bare, stony desert floor was a *carpet* of flowers!

"What happened? How can flowers grow from nothing?" I asked.

When we took off our goggles, there was the classroom, and everything was normal – if you can call Pickle Hill normal!

Rocky horror

Things didn't stay normal for long. Meena was first to notice the classroom walls.

"They're changing," she said slowly, "into solid rock."

Everyone went quiet, and most people's mouths dropped open so wide you could almost see the wobbly thing in their throats.

I was first up because I had trainers on, and the rest were close behind. Even so, when I stood up Miss Scorcher was right beside me. She took a deep breath. "Isn't it just magnificent?"

It was amazing! We were in a rocky desert. You'd think that might be flat and boring, but it wasn't. The weird-shaped rocks looked as if they'd been carved. There were tall pillars like factory chimneys, a massive mushroom-shaped one, and even a circular hole, like a window, in a ginormous wall of rock.

"They're like sculptures," I said.

"In a way, that's exactly what they are," said Miss Scorcher. "Wind and water are the sculptors."

"But how can wind sculpt rock?" asked Nita. "Wind feels like … like fresh air. How can it do anything to solid rock?"

"It has help," Miss Scorcher said. "There aren't many plants here to bind the soil together, so the wind whips up loose soil, sand, gravel and stones and blasts it against rocky surfaces. Over a long, long time, this blasting wears away the softer parts of rock."

"That's called erosion," said Will, all pleased with himself.

"Well done!" Miss Scorcher flashed him one of her smiles.

"Wa-hey!" Lizzie whispered in his ear. "Sandy loves Will!"

He kicked her.

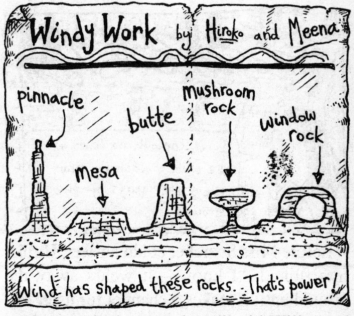

Windy Work by Hiroko and Meena

pinnacle

mesa

butte

mushroom rock

window rock

Wind has shaped these rocks. That's power!

"Our garden's on a slope," said Will, "and my dad's worried about the rain eroding away his strawberry patch."

Will's family worry just as much as he does!

"Water certainly is powerful," said Miss Scorcher. "When a rocky desert gets a year's worth of rain in just a few minutes, all that water has to go somewhere. Any ideas?"

"It soaks in?" wondered Arnie.

"What? Into bare rock?" I said, and jumped down into the gully.

Before Miss Scorcher could answer, Hiroko interrupted. "I know – it wears away the ground until it makes a channel for itself –"

"And every time it rains the channel gets deeper and deeper till it looks like this gully," Meena finished. "Right?"

Exactly what I'd have said – if I'd had a chance.

Everybody jumped down beside me. Except Miss Scorcher.

"Do you think the gully's a good place to be if it rains?" she asked.

"No way!" said Lucy Lee. "You'd get your feet wet."

"Listen," Miss Scorcher said. "What's that?"

There was a faint rumbly-roary sound. It got louder and louder. In slow motion, we all turned to look along the gully.

It was terrifying! Rocks and stones were hurled along by that great wall of water! If we stopped to climb out of the gully we'd be smashed to smithereens. And there was no way we could out-run it!

Just as the first splashes hit us, we stumbled, tumbled, landed in a heap, and I found myself staring at a piece of flattened chewing gum on a blue-tiled floor.

We were back in the classroom.

Phew! I have never, ever been so scared in my life. Poor Will lay on his back, quivering like a pool of jelly. I helped him up and we thumped each other to get the desert dust out of our clothes. And were we dusty!

"Ah-choo!" It only takes a speck of dust to get *me* going, but everybody round me was sneezing, too. Luckily, I always have a pocketful of tissues, and they know it. I passed them round as Miss Scorcher explained what had happened.

"That was a flash flood. Water can't soak into bare rocky ground, so it rushes through any channel it can find, washing away just about everything in its path. And before you ask, Will – that won't happen to your dad's strawberry patch!"

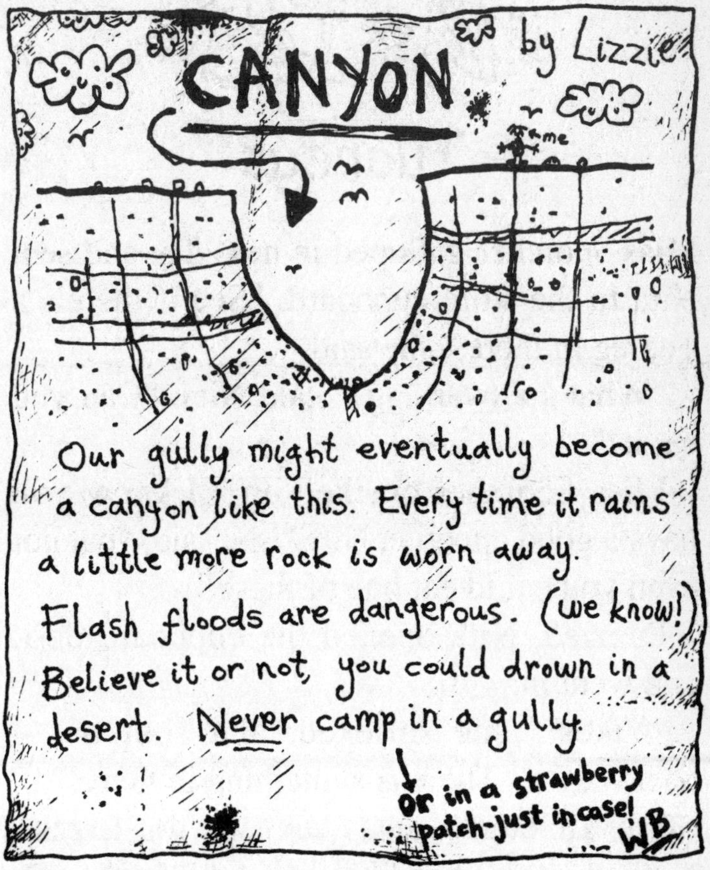

Tuaregs

Miss Scorcher galloped in next day and sent Nita to the store cupboard. "See if there's a Tuareg in there," she said.

"What's a twar egg?" said Nita. "Can you eat it?"

Miss Scorcher cracked up. "I know you have a good appetite, Nita," she said, "but not even you could eat one of these!"

Puzzled, Nita opened the cupboard door and went in.

"Yikes!" she shrieked, and shot out – backwards. "There *is* something in there!"

We all edged away, except for Lizzie. Nothing scares her. She pulled the door open. "It's not something," she said. "It's someone."

A small brown hand came round the edge of the door, followed by a pair of glittering dark eyes in a smiling face.

"This is Zara," said Miss Scorcher. "She's from a Tuareg family, who live in the Sahara Desert."

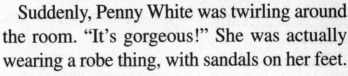

Greetings! I want to take you all home with me. But first you must dress like me.

Suddenly, Penny White was twirling around the room. "It's gorgeous!" She was actually wearing a robe thing, with sandals on her feet. Hey! We all were!

Like your frock, Fred!

Yours is Prettier!

The boys fell about, but Zara said they wouldn't last long in the Sahara in normal clothes.

We followed her into the cupboard, and into a low, wide and very hot tent! It seemed far too small to hold us all, but the whole class came through and we all fitted in, somehow.

"It's like an oven in here," Meena said.

"I feel a right nana in this dress thing," said Freddie. "I'm taking it off."

"You'd better check out what you're wearing underneath, first," said Hiroko.

Freddie peeked down the neck of his robe, and went bright red! Then we all did the same. Oo-er, what had happened to all our clothes?

Zara raised one side of the tent. The sun was a yellow glare, and there wasn't a cloud in sight. "Mohamed!" she called.

A young boy ran towards the tent and peered in. "Hello," he said.

"This is my brother," Zara explained.

Mohamed disappeared, calling to someone outside. "Mother, guess what Zara's done!"

"Oh no!" said a woman's voice. "Don't say we've got another tentful!"

A man, his head totally wrapped in blue cloth, ducked into the tent. He was followed by a woman with a veil draped over her head.

"Miss Scorcher!" said the man. "We're

always pleased to see *you*. Welcome – everyone! I am Malik. Let's have some tea." He sounded as if he was smiling, but we could only see his eyes as he shook hands with us. "You must eat with us, too."

Zara's mum, Yasmeen, looked a bit fed up. I could understand why. My mum says people only ever call when the place is a tip and there isn't a biscuit in the house. Zara's dad was demanding meals for a whole class!

"See?" said Zara. "We all wear cotton robes."

"If we didn't," said Malik, "the sun would burn us. We're called the people of the veil."

"This is a veil." Mohamed tossed Freddie a piece of blue cloth, about six metres long. "I'll wear one, when I'm a man."

Freddie tried to catch it. The cloth twisted out of his grasp, and turned and coiled and curled, until there was a turban on his head, and his face was completely covered, except for his eyes.

Yasmeen laughed so much she nearly dropped two pots she was making tea in.

"Tuareg men wear veils all the time," said Malik. "It is our tradition."

"Even when you eat?" Nita was aghast.

"Even then. It protects my head from the sun, and keeps sand from my mouth. My wife just drapes hers over her head but sometimes she holds it across her mouth, as Meena's doing."

Did I do that?

Malik laughed. "Tomorrow we move on, so it's a good thing you came today, isn't it, Yasmeen?"

62

"Oh, yes," she said, but her voice was just like my mum's when she's not being totally honest, but doesn't want to hurt your feelings.

"Why are you moving?" asked Gordon.

"We're nomads," said Malik. "We don't stay in one place."

NOMADS
by Hiroko

Nomads don't live in one place. They move on whenever they need more grass and stuff for their animals to eat. Their tents are easy to set up and pack away.

Zara's family neatly packed and ready to go.

ROGER'S REMOVALS

My family packed and ready to go.

We had three little cupfuls of tea each. It was hot and sweet, and made with mint. Hiroko hates tea, but Miss Scorcher said she must try. "It's rude to refuse," she whispered.

Mohamed took some of us outside.

Now I knew why the robes were best. The air could move about inside them. We'd have baked in jeans and T-shirts.

Yasmeen came out with some bowls and a little mat to sit on. Carrie Marsh's eyes were glued to her silver bracelet.

"Can Carrie try it on?" Zara asked.

Yasmeen held it out, and Carrie slipped it on her arm. "I love silver," she said.

"So do I," said Yasmeen. "And many good silversmiths are Tuareg," she added proudly.

Gordon asked how long they'd lived there.

"Ages and ages," said Mohamed. "Almost nineteen days."

"Nineteen days!" I gaped at him. "We live in our homes for years."

"But how do you feed your goats when the grass is gone?" he asked. "Don't you have to move to find fresh grazing?"

I realized he knew as little about us as we knew about him. "We don't keep goats," I said. "We have dogs and cats."

He looked as if he was about to yuck up. Before I could ask why, Zara came over and said, "Our animals are very important to us."

Nita called me just then, so I went to see what she wanted.

"Let's ask Yasmeen if we can help her get the food ready."

Oh, great – cooking. Just what I wanted to do in the desert – I *don't* think.

When Nita asked, Yasmeen did one of those pretend fainting acts. "Sorry," she said, "I'm not used to offers of help!"

There was no cooker. We had to make pancake thingies over a fire – outside the tent, of course. We peered into the bowl of pancake mixture.

"Yum," said Nita. "I'm starving."

That was nothing new, but I don't know how even she could fancy that stuff – it was all gloopy.

"There isn't enough to go round," I said
hopefully.

Yasmeen smiled. "Don't worry," she said,
"there's plenty."

And there was! I poured goats' milk into
bowls for everyone from a jug that never
seemed to empty, and Freddie and Arnie
passed round bowls of dates. I was glad of
them. They cheered up the pancake, which
was boring without syrup or sugar and lemon.
Nita had two.

"Do you eat meat?" Nita asked.

"Sometimes," said Zara.

"But there aren't any shops," Will said, "so
where do you get it?"

Zara waved a hand towards their animals. Will was really upset to discover their meat wasn't from a supermarket – it was walking round on four legs near the tent.

"You eat your animals?" he said.

"Of course. Don't you?"

Now I knew why Mohamed was disgusted when I said we had dogs and cats!

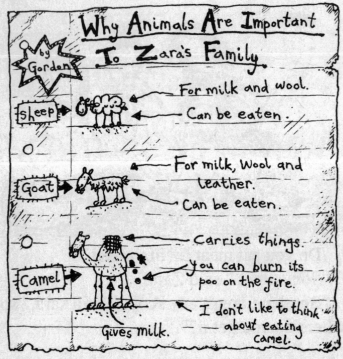

Why Animals Are Important
To Zara's Family

by Gordon

Sheep → For milk and wool.
Can be eaten.

Goat → For milk, wool and leather.
Can be eaten.

Camel → Carries things.
You can burn its poo on the fire.
I don't like to think about eating camel.
Gives milk.

"Zara!" called Malik. "Fetch some water, please."

Where would she get water from? There was no river in sight. "I'll come," I said, excited at the thought of a journey through the desert. I waved goodbye to my mates, and we set off.

Twelve paces later, Zara stopped under the tree and untied a shapeless bag from the lowest branch. I followed her back to the others. Everyone was trying not to laugh, and making a rubbish job of it.

"Good journey?" Freddie chuckled.

The bag was where they kept their water!

"We put things in the tree so the animals can't get at them," said Mohamed, "and we have to carry water with us, in goatskin bags."

Malik told us they camp near a well or waterhole when they can, but it's not always possible. "Then we have a long walk each day to fetch water."

"I do, you mean," said his wife. "When was the last time *you* fetched water?" She turned to us. "Women always get stuck with water-fetching."

"Do you ever go shopping?" asked Lucy Lee.

"We stop at a town sometimes, and swap our cheese and milk in the market, for money or food," said Zara.

"I like it when we come across a caravan," said Mohamed.

"A *what*?" said Hiroko. "In the *desert*?"

I giggled. "Not the sort of caravan you're thinking of! It's camels, isn't it, Mohamed?"

"A whole team of camels," he said, "piled with goods to sell or swap. Caravan leaders travel all over the place. When I grow up, that's what I want to do."

I gazed around. "Wouldn't you be afraid of getting lost? How do you find your way without maps or signposts?"

Yasmeen said there are landmarks, like mountain ranges and sticking-up rocks and stumps of dead trees, and they help. "Malik also goes by the sun and the stars," she said.

I reckon if you lived in the desert long enough, with no telly, you'd soon get to know what the stars look like. There'd be nothing else to look at once it got dark.

Miss Scorcher wandered out of the tent. "You'll rarely be short of stars for guidance in the desert," she said.

I remembered our homework about the desert being cold at night. "Is that because there aren't any clouds to hide them?"

"Partly," she said. "The stars aren't as clear where we live because there's so much light shining up into the sky from our towns and cities. Here, where night is truly dark, the stars are brighter and you can see many more. Close your eyes, count to five, then open them."

Day had turned to night – black, black night. As my eyes got used to the dark, little pinpoints of starlight began to glimmer, just a few at first. Then gradually, more and more appeared, until there must have been about a million.

We closed our eyes, counted backwards, and then it was light again, and Zara's mum said she'd better start organizing everything ready for moving on.

I hugged Zara and we all shook hands with her family, and ducked into the tent. I definitely hadn't seen a door in there, but there must have been one because suddenly we were back in the classroom and Miss Scorcher was closing the cupboard.

How *does* she do it?

Windy work

Next morning, Meena complained that we didn't see any sand dunes when we visited Zara.

"A large part of the Sahara is made up of the sort of stony plain we visited," said Miss Scorcher. "It's called reg. But the bit you're talking about is called erg."

Meena giggled. "Nita would like that. She's always hungry."

Nita stared. "Eh?"

"Erg and chips…" said Meena. "Erg sandwiches … Ergburger…"

"Oh, ha ha," said Nita. "Miss Scorcher, what is erg?"

"It's the Arab name for seas of sand. Almost a quarter of the Sahara is erg. Who'd like to see some dunes?"

Everybody shouted, "Me!"

"OK. Tess, open the book."

She hadn't given out any books. "Where is it?"

Miss Scorcher grinned. "Right under your nose!"

And it was. There, on my desk! As soon as I touched it, it opened at a picture of sand.

"It's not a dune," I said. "It's just a heap of sand."

"That's what a dune is, twit!" said Hiroko.

I glared, but Miss Scorcher chipped in: "Tess is right. A dune is created by the action of the wind, so until the wind's been to work on it, our heap of sand is just that – a heap."

Now it was Hiroko's turn to glare, and my turn to look smug.

Miss Scorcher asked me to lay the book on the floor. "Gather round," she said.

As we got up, the chairs and desks glided silently out of the way. Well, almost silently.

When we turned back, the book had grown! We have plenty of big books in our classroom, but none quite like this. It was the size of a carpet, and the heap of sand was evenly spread all over it.

"Now we need some wind," said Miss Scorcher.

Everyone looked at Nita, who could burp for Britain. She fell about and ended up with hiccups.

Pretending not to hear, Miss Scorcher handed us each a tube, like an extra-big straw. "Let's make dunes!" she said, and dropped a large stone in the sand.

She blew steadily through her tube. Gradually, the sand drifted until it covered the stone, and a dune began to form.

"It's like a crescent moon," said Gordon.

"Or a croissant," said Nita. "Hic!"

Hiroko, Freddie and I had a go.

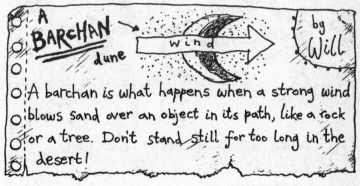

A BARCHAN dune — wind — by Will

A barchan is what happens when a strong wind blows sand over an object in its path, like a rock or a tree. Don't stand still for too long in the desert!

The sand levelled out again. Then Miss Scorcher got Nita, Meena, Penny, Gordon and Will all to blow in the same direction. Soon, a pattern of long ridges formed.

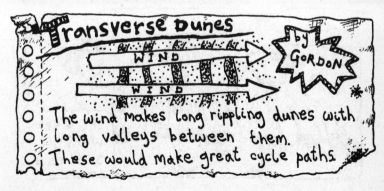

Transverse Dunes — WIND — WIND — by GORDON

The wind makes long rippling dunes with long valleys between them. These would make great cycle paths

When the sand flattened out again, Miss Scorcher told five of us to kneel in a circle and blow.

We huffed and puffed.

"It's a wonky star!" said Hiroko.

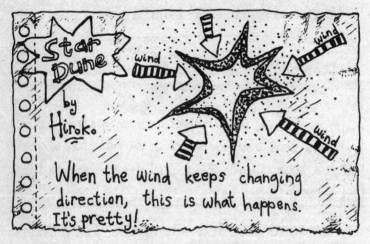

I sat back to admire it. Unfortunately, I felt a sneeze come on. I fished in my pocket and pulled out everything but a tissue. Too late.

"My turn." Miss Scorcher took a huge breath and blew. Flipping clever, she is. She seemed to blow in two different directions at once. Her dunes took a while to form, and when they did, they were just like the transverse dunes, only wiggly.

"Seif dunes," she announced.

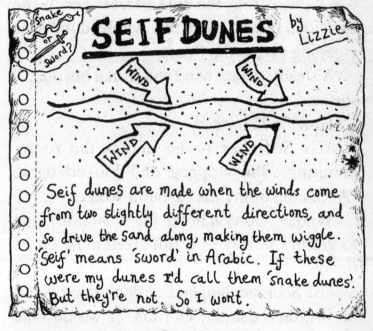

Miss Scorcher smiled. "Want to see a dune move?"

"Yes!"

"Then I need a large one."

"I'll make it," I said. Too late. Almost before I'd finished speaking, the sand heaved and shifted into a beautiful transverse dune.

"OK, let's move it!" Miss Scorcher blew towards the dune's base. Boy, did she blow! The sand whipped up over the top of the dune and down the other side. More and more sand was blown from the side nearest her to the far side. It was as if the whole dune was creeping across the floor!

"A steady strong wind can shift a big dune," she said.

"How far?" I asked.

Miss Scorcher paced across the room, counting. She stopped and looked back. "About ten of my paces, but it would –"

"Whoa!" Gordon broke in. "I wouldn't like to get in the way of a full-sized dune on its travels!"

Miss Scorcher laughed. "I don't think you'd be in much danger, Gordon. It would take about a year to move that far! Dunes are on the move all the time, though. Some have been known to move more than 25 metres a year."

"Imagine meeting a 20-metre high dune on the march," said Nita.

"That's nothing. It's perfectly normal to find dunes 40 metres high," said Miss Scorcher, "and I believe there's one that's 400 metres high! That's three times as high as the London Eye, and even higher than the Eiffel Tower."

We went home with our heads full of sand.

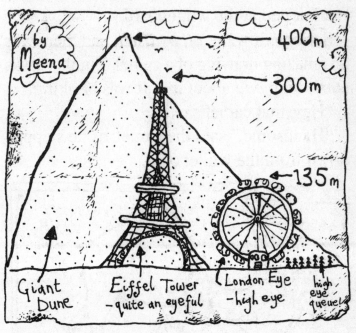

by Meena

400m

300m

←135m

Giant Dune

Eiffel Tower – quite an eyeful

London Eye – high eye

high eye queue!

Lawrence

In Friday's lesson, Miss Scorcher tossed a marker pen at the whiteboard.

Scribble it went, *all by itself*, and there was an amazing drawing of a camel. But there was something *odd* about it… It was blinking!

"Hey, that camel's…"

"Handsome," said the camel, as he stepped down from the whiteboard.

"You wouldn't smell too sweet if you'd spent seven years in the Sahara," said the camel, now full size.

"Is that where you live?" Lizzie asked.

The camel rolled his eyes. "Well, of *course* it is. Why else would I spend seven years there?"

Miss Scorcher coughed. "Ahem. Thank you, Lawrence." She turned to us. "Children, have a good look at Lawrence. Camels are unusual animals…"

Hrrumph!

"…and incredibly handsome," Miss Scorcher said, hurriedly. "Talk to Lawrence and see what you can find out." She winked and mouthed silently, "Be polite!"

Most of us went straight up to the camel, but Will and Hiroko hung back.

The camel gave Hiroko and Will a mean look and showed his teeth.

"You've got gorgeous eyelashes," said Nita.

That softened him. "I know," he said. Flutter, flutter.

"What's your hump for?" I asked.

"It's a sort of store," he explained. "It's full of fat, and if there isn't anything to eat, my body uses the fat as food. You can tell when I've used up the fat because my hump shrinks. Having a hump means I don't have to eat very often."

Meena laughed. "Nita gets the hump when she *can't* eat!"

"You're a dromedary, aren't you?" said Gordon.

Freddie was interested in Lawrence's long, strong legs.

"I can do 100 miles in a day on these," said the camel, proudly.

"Shame about your knees," said Lucy. "They're a bit scabby."

Lawrence turned a mean look on her. "So would yours be if you spent half your life getting up and down from them so people could climb on your back, and load you with baggage and –"

Miss Scorcher butted in quickly. "Lawrence works terribly hard, and we don't want to wear him out. Finish your questions, and we'll pool what we've discovered."

It was time for Lawrence to go, so we cleared a path and he padded across the room.

"Not that way!" Gordon yelled. "You can't go through the wall!"

Without turning, Lawrence muttered, "That's what you think, smarty pants." As he reached the wall, he went fuzzy – and was gone. Wicked!

Sand safari

Miss Scorcher hitched her bag on her shoulder and grabbed her bottle of Grillo Sun Cream Factor 55+. "What are you waiting for?" She dashed headlong into the wall, and then *she* was gone!

The others trickled after her. I was last. I closed my eyes and felt a tickly shiver as I went through, then, "Wow!" A blast of heat hit me and everything went bright. We were actually among the great Saharan sand dunes!

Miss Scorcher pulled hats from her bag for everyone – they all had a flap hanging over the back of the neck. I was startled to see we'd all got trousers on – whether we'd come to school in skirts or not.

"I want to get my legs brown," said Penny White. She rolled her trousers up but Miss Scorcher gave them one glance and they rolled themselves straight back down.

"Spend any time in the Sahara without protection, and you're asking for all sorts of nasty skin problems," she said, and told us to slap on plenty of Grillo. "You must wear robes, too."

"Which robes?"

"Those."

I didn't even bother to look down!

Lawrence had a bridle, and a comfy-looking saddle, and he looked magnificent.

"Down, Lawrence," said Miss Scorcher. "Watch, everyone. Riding a camel is quite an experience!"

Lawrence sank down with his feet tucked underneath, like a cat. Miss Scorcher climbed into the saddle. "Ready!"

Mount up, everyone.

Huh?

What's she on about?

Sun's boiled her brain.

Lawrence made a horrible honking sound. Answering honks came from behind, where our classroom used to be.

Padding steadily towards us, their feet flicking up sprays of sand, was a whole procession of camels.

"Whoo!" Freddie yelled. "Are they for us?"

Miss Scorcher nodded. "We're going on safari!"

"Sir what?" said Lizzie.

"A safari's a journey." Miss Scorcher was impatient to be off. "What are you waiting for? Get on board."

Lawrence honked, all the camels lay down, and we began the business of getting aboard. Now I knew why we wore trousers. Skirts would have been uncomfortable and, to be honest, I was glad to have my legs covered. Will reckoned the camels' coats were so dirty they probably had things living in them. They were dusty, too – I'd be sneezing before long.

"That wasn't so hard, was it?" said Miss Scorcher when we were all on board. "I hope you all saw what happened when Lawrence stood. Camels … *up!*" she ordered.

We were off!

Riding a camel's not like riding a horse. It moves both left legs together, then both right ones. As if that's not bad enough, it sways forwards and backwards, too.

Gordon's camel wandered off to the left.

"Hey, don't get lost," cried Will, but they soon wandered back.

We didn't have proper reins, just a rope. "How do you steer?" I wondered.

"With great difficulty!" said Gordon. "I'm having enough trouble staying on board!"

"You'll get used to it," called Miss Scorcher. "An expert uses his feet and the rope to guide the camel, but yours will follow Lawrence, and he's extremely intelligent…"

"Where are we going?" I yelled.

"To an oasis," Miss Scorcher shouted back, and on we went, swaying across the dunes.

We rode on for ages. Up a dune. Down a dune.

"Look!" Carrie pointed over to her left. "A lake!"

Oh, it looked so cool, but it was miles away.

"Sorry," said Miss Scorcher. "That's not water."

It's a mirage – a trick of the light that happens when it's so hot. What you see is the sky reflected in hot air near the ground. Because the reflection is blue and shimmery, it looks like water. If a camel walked across there, it would seem to be paddling.

We went round another dune, and there before us was a stunning sight. Right in the middle of all that sand were palm trees and a pool of water. It was no mirage. That water was real! Cool!

Oasis

"You can dismount now," said Miss Scorcher. "*Gordon*, NO! Wait till your camel lies down."

Lawrence grunted. "I'd tie that boy's legs together if I were you."

I found getting down easier than getting up.

The camels ambled off for a drink from the pool. They weren't the only ones. Freddie charged towards the water

Let me at it!

"Stop!" shrieked Miss Scorcher.

"Eh?" Water trickled through Freddie's cupped hands. "Why?"

"That's why!" I pointed to where a camel was weeing in the pool. "And it's probably full of bugs, anyway."

"Never forget!" said Miss Scorcher. "No one should drink water from pools or rivers without boiling it for ten minutes first, or using special chemicals to make it safe."

"Even then, you'd have to strain all the insect corpses out of it," said Lizzie.

Will spotted a spider near his foot and leapt a metre in the air.

This camel spider is only about 5cm long, but it's f-a-s-t. It can bite—hard. It eats insects, small birds, lizards, even scorpions. It eats so much it can hardly stagger home.
by Will

Miss Scorcher's bottomless bag produced a bottle of water. Each!

"Make it last," she said.

Hiroko stopped swigging water for a moment and asked, "Is this what all oasisis … oasisses…"

"Oases is the plural of oasis," Miss Scorcher said. "Oh-ay-sees."

"Is this what all oases look like?"

"They all have water," said Miss Scorcher, "so plant, animal and bug-life flourish round them."

So do people. Whole towns can grow up around an oasis, because where there's water, food can grow. And date palm trees like these. How useful do you think a date palm is?

You can eat the fruit at Christmas?

Or at Zara's!

"Gordon's right," said Miss Scorcher. "It's traditional to have a box of dates at Christmas. Desert people eat them at any time, though."

"Not just on special dates!" I said.

Everyone groaned, but they soon stopped when Miss Scorcher held out her hands and a basket of dates dropped into them.

She offered them round.

"There's loads here." Nita munched happily.

Miss Scorcher nodded. "You can get hundreds from just one bunch."

"Are the leaves any use?" asked Will. "Those look about five metres long!"

"This basket was woven from palm leaves," said Miss Scorcher. "Any other ideas?"

"Dates are fruit," said Gordon, "so they must have seeds."

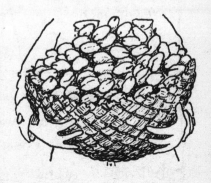

We had all been spitting out date stones as we ate, so we couldn't argue with that.

Tess's Date Palm

(fruit) You needn't wait till Christmas. Eat dates fresh or sun-dried (handy for long journeys). Grind the stones to feed Lawrence.

(leaves) Weave baskets, thatch roofs or make rope with fibres — from the leaves you could even make a hat!

(buds) You can eat the buds raw (I'd have to be desperate).

(sap) Sap comes out of the tree and it makes a drink. I prefer mine out of a bottle.

(trunk) Wood to make huts or furniture.

The thing we liked when we visited the tree was it shaded us, and if you see a date palm you know there's water nearby. But don't drink it!

"Seeds grow into new trees," Gordon went on. "That's useful."

Lawrence, who'd been snoozing, opened one eye. "Good nosh for camels, too," he murmured.

"If you chopped the tree down you could use the wood," I said, "but you wouldn't get the fruit then."

"You could wait till the tree dies, then chop it down," Lizzie suggested.

Miss Scorcher nodded. "You could, but you'd have to wait a long time – these trees can live twice as long as humans. Tess is right, though. The wood is great for building."

I wandered down to the pool's edge with Arnie.

"Where does it come from?" I muttered. "Why is there water just here?"

Arnie looked up, as if he expected to see a black cloud above us.

Miss Scorcher trotted over. "It doesn't come from the sky. It comes from underground. This water probably fell as rain miles away. It soaks into the ground and flows through aquifer rocks."

"What's aquifer?" I asked.

"Arnie can tell you tomorrow. It's his homework for tonight. The rest of you can choose any creature you like and see what you can discover about it."

How An Oasis Is Formed, by Arnie

1 Rain falls far away.

2 Water seeps underground in an aquifer — a layer of rock with tiny holes where water can get in.

3 Water comes up against a sort of wall, called a fault. It's forced upwards.

4 Pool full of water (and what camels do).

"Look!" said Arnie.

A pretty sandy and white bird was rocking around on the water.

"It's a sand grouse," said Miss Scorcher. "Interesting bird."

Interesting, eh? I bagged that one for my homework.

This male sand grouse has flown about 20 miles to collect water for his mate and chicks. He dunks his tum in the pool, and special feathers soak up water. Back at the nest, his chicks dip their beaks in his feathers. Now that's what I call a water bird!

by Tess Taylor

Everyone started searching for creatures for homework, but Will found a sand skink without even trying.

by Will Baker

The sand skink has smooth, shiny scales, and its square nose helps it dig. When it wants to burrow it 'swims' down into the sand, then wiggles like a fish through the cooler sand below the surface. Dinner? It pops its head up to the surface and grabs a nice juicy insect (it nearly grabbed me!).

And when Freddie met a lizard, he proved just how fit he really is. The lizard's tail would have spiked him if he hadn't moved so fast!

The spiny-tailed lizard is happy to be out and about during the day. If an enemy appears, it runs to its burrow, leaves its tail sticking out and whips it from side to side.

Does it work? Well, I wouldn't grab that tail!

by Freddie Field

Gordon didn't find a creature. A creature found him!

The desert hedgehog has a little pointy face, big ears to lose heat and for good hearing, eats insects and crunchy beetles. It lives in a burrow and has prickles. That's how I found him. Ouch!

Me and a Desert Hedgehog

by Gordon Budd

Soon we mounted up, and headed back through the desert. My camel rolled along so steadily I nearly dropped off to sleep, but a shout of "Whoa, Lawrence!" made me sit up. Where were we? There was nothing to be seen except a large boulder.

All the camels flumped to the ground and Miss Scorcher bounded out of the saddle. "Bye, Lawrence," she said and vanished behind the boulder.

Nobody moved.

"I'll have a look," said Lizzie. We got down and followed as she circled the boulder, giving it a wide berth.

"There's no one there," Lizzie said. "It must be the way back to the classroom." She edged forward cautiously, then gave an almighty scream as Miss Scorcher's head popped out of the boulder and said, "Come *on*, 5F!"

All we had to do was walk straight into the boulder. I closed my eyes, and I bet everybody else did, too. There was the tickly shiver, and when I dared to look, we were back outside the classroom window.

That was some school outing!

Desert secrets

After break on Monday, we bowled into class. The overhead projector was out ready.

"Sit down." Miss Scorcher's voice came from the back of the room. She was standing by the window in the sunlight, and she *sparkled*!

Gordon whistled, Penny went green with envy, and Ben Lee's eyes were like gobstoppers.

Miss Scorcher dripped with jewels! A tiara on her head, earrings like bunches of grapes, bracelets on both arms, rings on her fingers, and I wouldn't have minded betting she had bells on her toes.

We sat at our desks, staring as the jewels flashed and glittered.

"Move to where you can see the screen," she said.

Still sitting, we shuffled and jumped our chairs forward, making a horrible noise. As soon as we were settled, the curtains closed.

I sat with my feet up on Hiroko's chair. The projector light came on, showing a sandy desert scene, just like on our Sahara trip. Then the scene shifted to the right and showed a road – a proper tarmac road – and some low, plain buildings and machinery.

I was about to ask Miss Scorcher if this had anything to do with her diamonds and stuff, when a man stuck his head round the corner of the picture and everybody screeched.

"This is Jerry," said Miss Scorcher. "So far, we've seen that deserts can be pretty empty spaces –"

"Pretty *scary* spaces," Will put in.

"But there's more to deserts than animals and floods and rain, isn't there, Jerry?"

"Yep," he said.

Miss Scorcher waited. We all waited. The only sound was Nita's tummy rumbling.

"Jerry?" said Miss Scorcher. "You work in the oil business, don't you? In the Arabian Desert?"

"Yep."

Miss Scorcher was getting ratty – you could tell because she had her legs crossed and one foot was going up and down like a high-speed seesaw.

She took a deep breath. "There are vast pools of oil trapped in the rocks beneath the sands. Jerry and his workmates get it out and send it in huge pipes to big refineries. It's sold around the world, isn't it, Jerry?"

"Yep," he said.

"And it's made the owners of the land very rich, hasn't it, Jerry?"

Miss Scorcher slid her chair towards the overhead projector. "I'm sure you're in a hurry, Jerry," she said. "Thank you *so* much. You've been *such* a help ... and *so* full of information."

"You're welcome," he said, "my job can be a bit lonely, so it's good to talk."

"We'd never have guessed," Lizzie grunted.

"He certainly didn't have much to say," muttered Miss Scorcher, as she switched the projector – and Jerry – off, "and he definitely won't be taking part in my lessons again. Waste of space."

Lizzie turned and mouthed, "Too busy eyeing up Miss Sandy Scorcher, if you ask me."

Everyone honked with laughter.

"She hasn't said why she's all done up in diamonds," Hiroko complained.

Miss Scorcher heard her. She smiled mysteriously. "No, 'she' hasn't!"

"Has oil really made people rich?" Carrie asked.

"It's made countries like Saudi Arabia fantastically wealthy," said Miss Scorcher, "and that's meant new hospitals and schools for the people. Also, the oil business means jobs to people who might never have had a hope of work before the oil deposits were discovered."

"Is there anything else in the desert that makes money?" I asked.

"I'll say." Miss Scorcher rubbed her hands together. "Over the years, fortunes have been made from copper, natural gas, salt –"

"Salt!" said Lizzie. "How can you make money from salt? You buy it in the supermarket."

"Deserts have been mined for salt for thousands of years." Miss Scorcher shot over to the windowsill and whipped the dish from beneath our spider plant. "Oh dear," she said, peering into it. "No water."

"Be a miracle if there was!" said Hiroko. "Tess is plant monitor this term."

I never remember.

"Imagine this dish is an old dried-up lake."

"That's easy, eh, Tess?" Hiroko giggled.

"There's a sudden rainfall," said Miss Scorcher, "and the lake fills up. See?"

She showed us the dish, and sure enough, there was a "lake" in it.

Meena shook her head. "I don't know how she does it."

"What's this got to do with salt?" asked Carrie.

"The salt that's in the soil mixes with the water. Then the sun gets to work on it."

Miss Scorcher darted to the windowsill and held the dish in the sun. "We'll speed things up a little," she said, with a wink.

Within 30 seconds the water had completely evaporated, and she showed us a dish – of salt! It was quite crusty.

I wouldn't put that on my chips.

"Salt has always been big desert business," said Miss Scorcher. "In Roman times it was so valuable that soldiers were paid an allowance just so they could buy salt. They called it their 'salarium'."

Hiroko said, "My mum's a sales rep, and she gets a salary."

"Excellent connection, Hiroko! The word 'salary' does come from 'salarium'."

"My mum's doesn't," said Hiroko. "It comes from the wages department."

Meena snorted, but Hiroko ignored her. "What else is there in the desert?" she asked.

"Solar power stations harness the sun's energy and turn it into electricity. That's used to pump water for irrigation."

Freddie asked what we all wanted to know. "What's irrigation?"

"Desert land can be made to grow crops," said Miss Scorcher, "but you need a lot of water to turn it green. Using electricity, water can be pumped from deep underground."

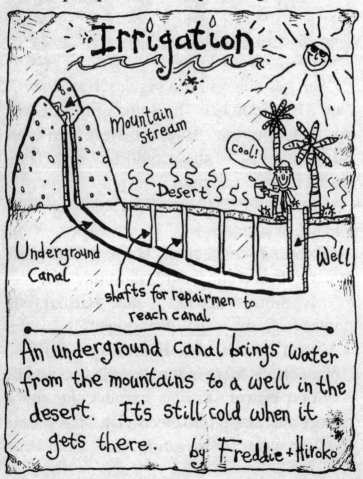

Irrigation

Mountain Stream

Cool!

Desert

Underground Canal

shafts for repairmen to reach canal

Well

An underground canal brings water from the mountains to a well in the desert. It's still cold when it gets there. by Freddie + Hiroko

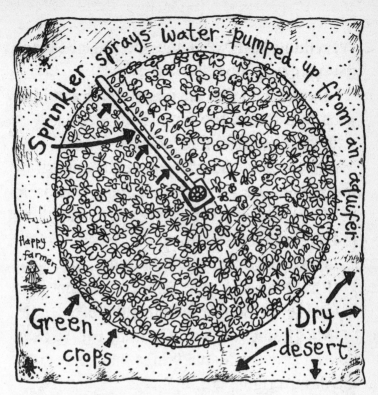

Sprinkler sprays water pumped up from an aquifer

Happy farmer

Green crops

Dry desert

That made me think. "If deserts are getting greener, they must be getting smaller, right?"

"I'm afraid not," said Miss Scorcher. "In many places, deserts are actually growing. It happens for all sorts of reasons. Sometimes there isn't even the usual amount of rain."

I remembered the Tuaregs. "If people like Zara let their animals eat all the plants, the ground will soon turn dry and dusty."

"Exactly," said Miss Scorcher. "Take away

everything that holds the soil together, and the wind will blow the soil away."

I shivered. "I like the desert, but I wouldn't want it to spread too far."

"People are trying to stop the spread," said Miss Scorcher. "In some areas, they put straw mats over the ground and plant shrubs in between, or they plant lots of trees – anything to help hold the soil down."

"Must cost a lot," said Gordon.

"It's expensive," she agreed, "but that land is vital to the people who live there."

"Miss Scorcher," said Gordon, "we've been talking about valuable things that come from the desert, right?"

She smiled. "Ye-es."

"Are you wearing a clue?"

"I am!" She rattled her bracelets and flashed her rings. "All these precious metals and gem stones came from deserts. And that's your homework – find out which desert each jewel came from."

We rushed up for a closer look. It was hard to believe all that jewellery came from the desert. Well, almost all!

Miss Scorcher's Desert Rocks

Tiara: diamonds from the Namib (Princess Sandy!)

Earrings: silver and turquoise from North American deserts (made by Navajo Indians)

Rings: Opals from Australia (they're called black opals, she says, but they're grey and blue)

Bracelets: gold from the Sahara and copper from the Atacama

Necklace: leather and silver from Sparkles in the High Street (ultra cool!)

(bit over the top, 3 or 4 would have done)

Belly button ring: gold from Australia (we didn't see this, but she swore it's there, so we've drawn it)

115

Gobi

On Wednesday afternoon, Miss Scorcher looked very different. She was wrapped in layers of woollen clothes and fur-lined skins, and in place of her normal cap she wore a striped woolly hat, like my Gran's tea cosy.

"This is our last lesson –" said Miss Scorcher.

We all groaned.

"– and this time we're going to visit a very different desert, and find out something about its past."

Miss Scorcher pulled a roll of shiny orange fabric and a pile of atlases from her bag. She passed the books round. "Who can find the Gobi Desert?"

"Oh oh," said Carrie. "That's one of the freezing-cold winter ones, isn't it? Now I know why she's wearing all that gear."

Miss Scorcher pinned up the orange fabric. It unrolled, almost to the floor, and hung there, rippling gently. "As you know where it is, Gordon," she said, "you can lead us there."

"Where?"

"The Gobi."

"*Where?*"

"Go behind the orange silk screen."

"Oh, good one, Miss Scorcher," said Lizzie. "Gobi-hind … ha ha."

Gordon hung back, but Lizzie shoved him aside and said, "*I'll* lead." She lifted the orange silk, slipped behind it and was gone. Really gone – there wasn't even a bump where you'd expect her to be.

We followed, one by one, and found ourselves on a stony path cut into a bare rocky hillside. It was pretty obvious that this was the Gobi. The air was co-o-old. Thankfully, we were now wrapped up in thick warm coats made of some sort of skin. But they smelled disgusting.

Miss Scorcher's voice cut through our grumbles. "Skins are the best way for Gobi dwellers to keep warm in winter. As you can see, there's nowhere to buy clothes, so they have to use what's handy."

"And that means animals," said Will sadly.

Miss Scorcher stretched up and peered along the path. "We're about to meet people who are selling something. A caravan's due any minute."

The thought of a nice cosy little caravan to curl up in was cheering – until I remembered that a caravan was a load of camels on the move.

"How many camels make a caravan?" asked Gordon.

Everybody shrieked back, "We don't know – how many camels do make a caravan?"

But Gordon didn't laugh. "No, it's not a joke. I'm serious. How many is it, Miss Scorcher?"

She shrugged. "Any number, from three or four, to thousands. Hey! Here they come!" She sped hotfoot towards a long string of heavily laden camels.

We followed more slowly.

The leader stopped. "Greetings, my lady."

"Greetings," said Miss Scorcher. "I've brought some young travellers to meet you."

He looked around. "And where is your man?"

"I haven't got one," said Miss Scorcher, and gave him one of her brilliant smiles.

"Oh flip," said Lizzie. "He won't be able to take his eyes off her now." She bounced up to the man. "Where are you from?" she demanded.

He turned his gaze towards her. "You are bold, girl."

"Oh please tell us," begged Miss Scorcher.

We are from China, in the East. We carry silk to Western lands, and charge a lot of money for it.

"Your sums are wrong," said Hiroko. "It's more than 2,000 years since 100 BC. This *is* the 21st century, you know."

The man looked down his nose. "Girl, *you* are wrong. The year is 1325."

We slowly turned to Miss Scorcher. Our eyes must have been as big as Brussels sprouts.

"We've travelled back over 600 years," she said. "We're at the edge of the Gobi Desert, on the famous Silk Road."

Freddie looked down. "Looks like ordinary dirt and stones to me."

Caravan on the

Caravanserai — a sort of desert motel. It had a courtyard with rooms round it, and stables underneath (bit smelly in summer). Traders could stop here for the night.

Sick Man: He's ill, so he's riding in a pannier. That's why it's good to travel together.

Road Over 4,000 miles long.

China this way

Caravans might have carried:
- tea, silk and jade from China
- Spices from India
- gold from Africa
- packed lunch
- change of underwear

The leader reached into his saddlebag and pulled out a length of shimmering crimson material embroidered with deep blue dragons.

"A gift for a beautiful lady," he said to Miss Scorcher.

Lizzie snorted in disgust. "I knew he fancied her."

Miss Scorcher's face went so red it almost matched the silk. "Wow! Thanks!"

The camel drivers moved on their stately way.

Miss Scorcher wrapped the fabric round her shoulders, like a shawl. "The Chinese carefully kept the secret of silk-making for hundreds of years," she said, "but eventually it leaked out. It's said that a Roman Emperor sent two monks to China to bring back some silkworms and they smuggled out some cocoons in a hollow walking stick."

"Cocoons? Why?" asked Arnie.

Silkworms & Cocoons

by Miss Scorcher

"Because each cocoon contained a silkworm, so the Emperor was able to start breeding his own. And every cocoon of every silkworm – which is really a caterpillar – is spun from silk. It's strong, but delicate – and you need over 100 cocoons to make a tie!"

Miss Scorcher glanced at the camel train as it plodded on. "By the end of the 16th century that caravan would be a rare sight. Sea routes opened up between east and west making trade easier and quicker. And we must be quick, too." She checked her watch. "Nearly home time! Let's go!"

She zoomed downhill, the crimson silk flowing behind her like a river in the air.

Just then, I spotted something green and gold in the middle of the Silk Road. I picked it up. It felt soft and cool, and seemed to flow over my fingers.

It was silk. The caravan leader must have dropped it. I knew it was valuable, so I ran after them.

"Hey!" I panted, as I reached the leader. "You dropped this!"

He gazed down at me. "You may keep it, as a gift from my century to yours. It is a kerchief for you."

"Thanks very much," I said politely. What I really meant was, "Thanks a bunch!" If I'd known he didn't want it, I wouldn't have chased after him.

I stroked my kerchief – I suppose he meant handkerchief – as I walked back. The green silk was embroidered with pink blossom and long-legged golden birds. It was far too beautiful to wipe your nose on, though, and when I really thought about how old it was, my mind boggled. I reckoned I might put it in a glass case or something. A 14th-century silk kerchief was something to treasure!

I tucked it in my pocket and broke into a run, keen to tell the others.

But the others had gone!

Below me on the hillside I caught a flash of crimson. Miss Scorcher's silk! I had to reach it. If it disappeared, I wouldn't have a clue how to get back and I'd be lost in time –

stranded for ever!

I stumbled and slid on loose stones as I galloped down the hill after the only link between the Silk Road and Pickle Hill. With a mighty effort, I leapt and grabbed a corner.

Instantly, the silk wrapped itself round and round me, from top to toe. I felt myself falling…

falling…

falling…

"Ooof!" I landed on the burst beanbag.

A hand pulled the silk from my face. Miss Scorcher's eyes twinkled at me. "Welcome back, Tess."

Everyone was raving about the desert. Lizzie sniffed her hands. "We still stink a bit," she said, "but who cares! I've had a fantastic time! Deserts are magic!"

"Brush yourselves down before you go home," said Miss Scorcher. "Deserts are dusty places too!"

She was right – we were filthy. We thumped and banged our clothes, raising clouds of dust.

Lizzie's nose twitched, and her eyes screwed up. "Tess! Tissue, quick!"

I reached into my pocket. "Here you go!"

"Ah-choo!" she sneezed. Then she stared at her hand.

So did I. I couldn't believe my eyes.

Lizzie West had just *ruined* my beautiful 600-year-old silk kerchief.